C000203289

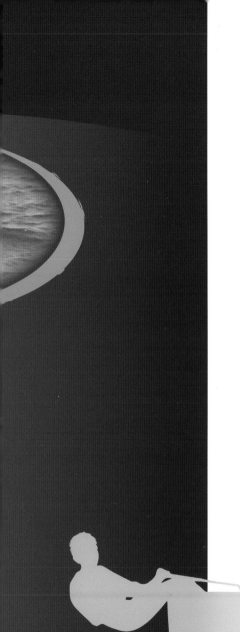

Introduction

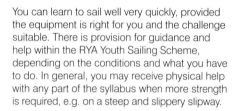

The RYA Youth Sailing Scheme provides an enjoyable and progressive way to learn to sail. Each certificated course provides an opportunity to recognise your achievements.

Your instructor will sign off each skill as you complete it. Once completed, an RYA certificate will be issued, showing your significant achievement. Your certificate can be of use in contributing to other areas of your study, activities, or the Duke of Edinburgh Award Scheme.

The RYA Youth Sailing Scheme is usually completed in small dinghies suitable for your size. However, it can also be completed in keelboats and multihulls with some changes to the syllabus and course, e.g. no capsize drill in keelboats.

You can learn to sail well very quickly, provided the equipment is right for you and the challenge suitable. There is provision for guidance and help within the RYA Youth Sailing Scheme, depending on the conditions and what you have to do. In general, you may receive physical help with any part of the syllabus when more strength is required, e.g. on a steep and slippery slipway.

Make sure you can perform all the skills in one course before tackling the next one; otherwise you may waste time relearning skills, or even fail to complete all of the new course.

In this logbook 'With instruction' means 'Can perform the task with a briefing for the conditions, and physical assistance if necessary'.

Courses in the RYA Youth Sailing Scheme are of a minimum length of 16 hours, two days or an equivalent series of sessions. Sailing is a sport that gets better with practice, and you should try to sail between courses whenever possible. Practice makes perfect!

Sailors who are unable to complete parts of the syllabus due to a disability may still receive a certificate, endorsed as necessary, e.g. 'Needs assistance with capsize drill'.

Take a challenge

'TAKE A CHALLENGE AND LOG YOUR RESULTS'

At the end of each stage, and not part of the main course or certificate, are some fun things for you to try. Get your instructor to sign the book to say you have completed them!

Each 'Take a Challenge' is designed to improve your skills and techniques in all aspects of sailing by just being out on the water and having fun!

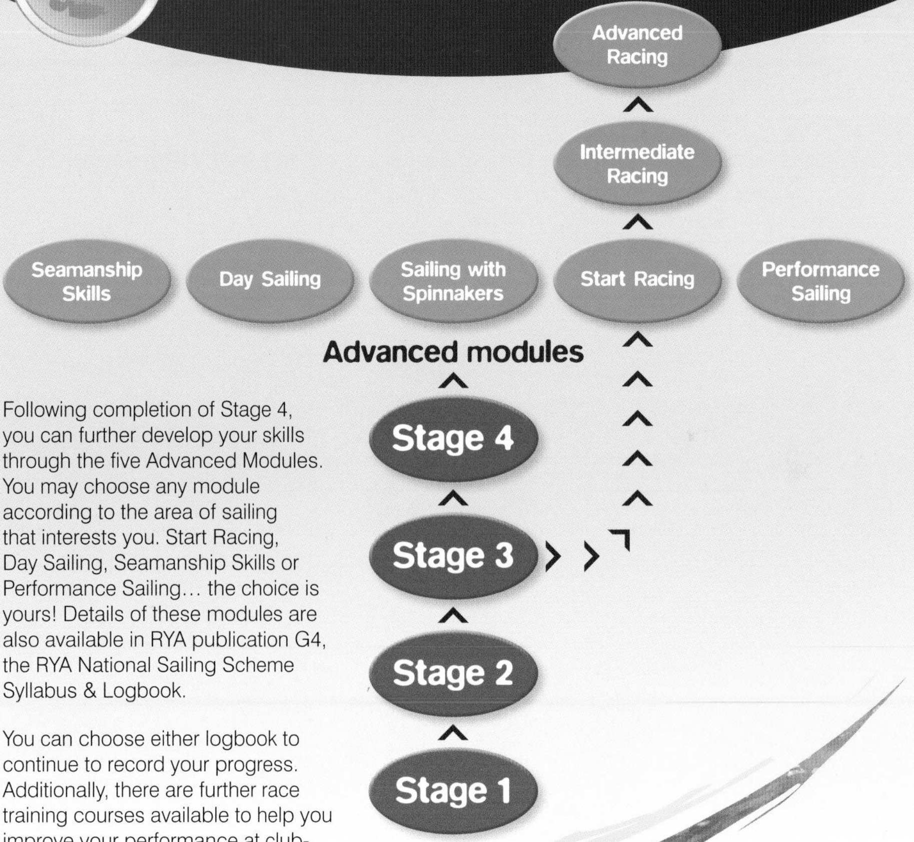

CHALLENGE

Advanced Racing

^

Intermediate Racing

^

| Seamanship Skills | Day Sailing | Sailing with Spinnakers | Start Racing | Performance Sailing |

Advanced modules

Stage 4

Stage 3

Stage 2

Stage 1

Following completion of Stage 4, you can further develop your skills through the five Advanced Modules. You may choose any module according to the area of sailing that interests you. Start Racing, Day Sailing, Seamanship Skills or Performance Sailing… the choice is yours! Details of these modules are also available in RYA publication G4, the RYA National Sailing Scheme Syllabus & Logbook.

You can choose either logbook to continue to record your progress. Additionally, there are further race training courses available to help you improve your performance at club-racing level. Happy sailing!

GET ON BOARD

RYA
OnBoard

It's time for you to get OnBoard!

If you're aged 8 to 18, OnBoard makes it super easy for you to get into sailing with the RYA Youth Sailing Scheme.

Why would you want to? That's the easy part…

Sailing is awesome fun. You can get a mad buzz from going fast, get competitive by learning to race, or just have a laugh hanging out on the water with your friends.

OnBoard's been making the RYA Youth Sailing Scheme safe and simple to get into for hundreds of thousands of kids all over the country since 2005. If you live near the sea, a river, a lake, a reservoir or an estuary, you can get OnBoard.

You don't need a boat, you don't need kit, you just need you. OnBoard does the rest.

Oh, and sailing teaches you heaps of cool life skills too! OnBoard focuses on developing creativity, confidence, teamwork, communication, determination, and independence.

CREATIVITY

Creativity involves having good ideas, dealing with uncertainty, and being able to make links between apparently unconnected things. Creative people have made great discoveries through seeing connections where others have not.

CONFIDENCE

Being confident involves being a can-do person, and being able to act independently. We gain more self-belief when we understand that making mistakes is normal, and know that the smart thing to do is to put in extra effort to work hard to improve.

TEAMWORK

Being a team player requires the ability to listen, show kindness to others, and give and receive feedback well. Giving helpful feedback is a difficult skill, but once learned it is very useful in many situations and an essential element of effective teamwork.

COMMUNICATION

Communicating well is very important. A lot of unhappiness comes from accidental misunderstandings or careless explanations. Communication involves learning how to offer opinions. It also includes how to match language to the audience or person receiving the communication.

DETERMINATION

Determination involves coping with difficulty. When we get stuck, we need to have strategies for getting unstuck! Sometimes we also need to know how to bounce back after setbacks, rather than giving up.

INDEPENDENCE

Independence is not just about learning to do things yourself. It's also about knowing how to get the best out of those around you. Becoming independent is a fundamental part of growing up, and includes making decisions and dealing with responsibility.

Taking the next step and getting involved is easy. The OnBoard programme runs at over 250 RYA-approved OnBoard sailing and windsurfing clubs and centres throughout the UK, and is open to anyone aged 8–18. For more detailed information and to find your nearest OnBoard club or centre, visit rya.org.uk/onboard, email us at onboard@rya.org.uk or call us on 02380 604 100.

PRACTICAL

Rigging

Can assist with rigging a boat.

Launching & Recovery**

Can launch a dinghy and get under way with instruction.

Can secure boat to trolley.

Can assist with recovery and stowage of dinghy and gear.

Ropework

Can tie a figure of eight knot and cleat a halyard.

Sailing Techniques & Manoeuvres

Can be a responsive crew under instruction.*

Can steer when sailing and being towed.

Can steer on a reach and go about (reach to reach).

Understands the effect of basic boat controls.

Understands the basic principles of stopping, controlling speed and getting out of irons.

Can paddle or row (with sprit, paddle or oars).

Can call for assistance.

Clothing & Equipment

Can put on personal buoyancy correctly.

Is confident in the water wearing personal buoyancy.

Capsize Recovery

Understands the importance of staying with the boat.**

SAILING BACKGROUND

Can name basic parts of a boat (i.e. hull, mast, rudder, tiller, centreboard, sheets etc.).

Understands what action to take to assist those needing help.

Understands how to prepare for a tow.

Clothing & Equipment

Understands personal safety – and knows what to wear for sailing (including head and footwear).

Meteorology

Has knowledge of wind direction.

OTHER ASPECTS AND OPTIONS

- The Stage 2 course.
- Regular activity (Clubs/Onboard).

*Not singlehanders
**Not keelboats

ALL SECTIONS COMPLETED

Instructor's signature   Centre stamp

TAKE A CHALLENGE

▷ Can you clap your hands while sailing?

▷ Why not challenge your friends to see who can rig the quickest?

▷ Starting from the beach as a group, sail or paddle out to a buoy and return to the shore. Perhaps even get into teams and make the challenge into a relay!

By the end of this introductory course you will have a basic understanding of how a boat sails, and some experience of steering and handling the boat. Stages 2, 3 and 4 will complete your introduction to the sport in easy stages.

PRACTICAL

Rigging

Can put a boat head to wind for rigging.

Can rig a dinghy.

Launching & Recovery**

Understands how to manoeuvre a trolley clear of other boats and overhead cables.

Can launch and recover a small dinghy.

Ropework

Can tie a round turn and two half hitches and a reef knot.

Sailing Techniques & Manoeuvres

Can control speed, and stop by lying-to.

Can get out of irons.

Can go about (close reach to close reach).

Can crew a boat effectively.*

Can sail a shallow triangle across the wind under supervision (gybing optional).

Understands the Principles of:

The five essentials.

Returning to a beach** or pontoon.

Capsize Recovery**

Can be scooped in during capsize recovery*

or

Can right one type of dinghy.

*Not singlehanders
**Not keelboats

SAILING BACKGROUND

Sailing Manoeuvres

Understands the No Go Zone.

Understands what is meant by windward, leeward and gybe.

General

Has knowledge of:

Spars and rigging.

Parts of the sail.

Sail controls and foils.

Offshore and onshore winds.

Knows the importance of telling someone ashore you are going afloat.

The dangers of man-made hazards, e.g. overhead power lines, weirs.

Rules of the Road

Has knowledge of port/starboard rule.

Meteorology

Understands several ways of finding wind direction.

Clothing & Equipment

Can choose and correctly adjust a personal buoyancy aid.

Understands what to wear.

OTHER ASPECTS AND OPTIONS

- The Stage 3 course.
- Opportunities for regular practice.
- Club activity.

ALL SECTIONS COMPLETED

Instructor's signature   Centre stamp

8

TAKE A CHALLENGE

▷ Get your instructor to write the parts of a boat on a card. Have a race with your group and see who can label them the quickest!

▷ Can you drag one leg in the water while sailing along?

▷ Ask your instructor to set up a race with a difference. At some marks you will score high being first, but at others you aim to be last! This will really test your boat control!

By the end of this course you will have a range of sailing skills and background knowledge, and be well on the way to being a confident small-boat sailor.

PRACTICAL

Rigging, Launching & Recovery**

Can rig, launch and recover in a variety of winds.

Can reef a dinghy ashore according to weather conditions.

Can store a dinghy ashore.

Ropework

Can tie a bowline, clove hitch and rolling hitch.

Sailing Techniques & Manoeuvres

Can demonstrate the basic principles of the following:

The five essentials –

Sail setting.

Balance.

Trim.

Course made good.

Centreboard.

Sailing on all points of sailing on a triangular course.

Tacking upwind.

Gybing from a training run.

Righting a small capsized dinghy as helm/crew.**

Coming alongside a moored boat.

Prepare for/take up tow from power craft.

Picking up a mooring.

Racing

Understands the course and starting procedure.

SAILING BACKGROUND

Manoeuvres

Understands how to and can recover a man overboard.

Understands the points of sailing.

General

Understands how a sail works – basic aerodynamics.

Knows basic terminology for use afloat (windward, leeward, bear away, luff up).

Understands the importance of clear communication aboard.

Understands lee shore dangers and sailing in close company with other water users.

Understands advice to inland sailors for coastal sailing.

Knows the importance of personal safety and telling someone ashore.

Understands the dangers of hypothermia and the use of correct clothing for protection.

Rules of the Road

Knows the basic rules of the road – port/starboard, windward boat and overtaking boat.

Meteorology

Knows how to obtain a weather forecast.

Understands Beaufort Wind Scale.

Knows when to reef.

Clothing & Equipment

Understands the importance of:

Personal safety equipment.

Boat buoyancy.

Basic safety equipment, e.g. anchor, paddle, bailer.

*Not singlehanders

**Not keelboats

ALL SECTIONS COMPLETED

Instructor's signature

Centre stamp

OTHER ASPECTS AND OPTIONS

- The Stage 4 Course.
- Regular practice and club activity.
- An introduction to the Racing Syllabus and the Start Racing Course.

TAKE A CHALLENGE

▷ Can you sail a triangular course with no centreboard?

▷ Scatter balls in a sailing area set by your instructor and see who can collect the most out of your group of friends when returning them to your instructor's boat.

▷ Ask your instructor to lay a box course. The aim is to see who can stay within the box the longest without being forced out by the other boats.

Having completed Stage 3 you will be able to sail in any direction and rig and launch your boat. Your skills and knowledge mean that you can regard yourself as a sailor, not a beginner.

PRACTICAL

Rigging & Launching

Can:

Rig

Launch

Recover

in any wind direction.

Can set up a boat according to weather conditions using sail and rig controls, e.g. mast rake, reefing.

Ropework

Knows the uses of and can tie:

Figure of eight.

Round turn and two half hitches.

Reef knot.

Bowline.

Clove hitch.

Rolling hitch.

Sheet bend.

Sailing Techniques & Manoeuvres

Can demonstrate:

Sailing techniques and manoeuvres from Stage 3 in a crewed boat.

Communicate effectively as helm and crew.

Effective use of the five essentials by helm and crew afloat including use of tell-tales.

Recovering a man overboard.

Returning to a beach,** jetty or mooring safely in any wind direction.

*Not singlehanders

**Not keelboats

SAILING BACKGROUND

Has knowledge of:

IRPCS.

Beaufort Scale.

Synoptic charts.

Tidal ebb and flow.

Spring and neap tides.

Knows how to recover from total inversion.**

COASTAL (OPTIONAL)

Can apply practical sailing techniques and manoeuvres on tidal waters.

Sailing Background

Can apply the IRPCS afloat.

Has basic knowledge of IALA buoyage, how to use tide tables and how to find the direction of tidal streams.

OTHER ASPECTS AND OPTIONS

- Advance your skills with one of the Advanced Modules.
- RYA Racing Pathway options.
- Regular practice and club activity.
- Start your progression to becoming an Assistant Instructor and volunteering at your local club or centre.

ALL SECTIONS COMPLETED

Instructor's signature   Centre stamp

TAKE A CHALLENGE

- See if you can learn to sail your boat backwards.
- Can you tie three knots blindfolded?
- Ask your instructor to lay a course setting a challenge to see how many tacks and gybes you can complete on the upwind and downwind legs.

A Stage 4 certificate means that you have the skills to sail a double-handed boat as crew or helm, and solve a variety of problems afloat. Passing this course is the natural entry point for the advanced courses.

Once you have learned to helm and crew a small boat, all sorts of opportunities in sailing are open to you...

Advanced Modules

As in all sports, practice is essential if you are to improve your skills and the best way to become a good sailor is to sail a variety of types of boats in different conditions.

Having practised your skills, one of the best ways to try a different type of sailing is to take another RYA course.

Following Stage 4, you have a choice of Advanced Modules in the RYA National Sailing Scheme. All of these can be run in two days, or an equivalent series of sessions over a longer period of time. Each course will introduce you to a different type of sailing, and may involve other classes of boat, depending on what is available locally.

Seamanship Skills

Seamanship skills will help you learn skills a short step beyond Stage 4. During this course you will polish and test your skills and learn to resolve problems afloat.
The course will give you a solid foundation for the future and enable you to become much more confident and self-sufficient afloat.

PLACE SIGNATURE HERE

PRACTICAL

Ropework

Can tie a fisherman's bend and sheet bend.

Can do heat sealing & whipping.

Launching & Recovery

Can leave and return to beach, jetty or mooring:

Windward shore.

Leeward shore.

Sailing Techniques & Manoeuvres

Is able to:

Heave to

Reef afloat

Recover MOB

Be towed

Anchor†

Sail backwards

Sail in adverse circumstances**†

Knows how to prepare road trailer and secure ashore.

COASTAL OPTION

Capable of practical application of skills in coastal waters.

Can use local tide tables.

Understands Rule of Twelfths and is aware of tidal streams.

Has a basic understanding of charts and important symbols.

SAILING BACKGROUND

Sailing Theory

Understands terminology: windward, leeward, abeam, forward, aft, ahead, astern, to weather, downwind, amidships, quarter, pinching, sailing by the lee, luff, bear away, planing, sternway, broaching.

Knows and can apply the following International Regulations for the Prevention of Collisions at Sea (IRPCS):

Meeting other sailing vessels.

Meeting power driven vessels.

Following or crossing narrow channels.

Action by stand-on vessel.

Capsize Recovery

Knows how to recover from total inversion.

Meteorology

Knows sources of information on weather patterns for day.

Can interpret forecasts and understand local effect.

Aware of Beaufort Scale and changing weather conditions.

**Not necessarily applicable to keelboats
†Not necessarily applicable to multihulls

ALL SECTIONS COMPLETED

Instructor's signature   Centre stamp

16

Experienced Sailor's Direct Assessment

Sailors must satisfactorily complete the practical elements and answer questions on the theory sections. Candidates seeking assessment on coastal waters will demonstrate knowledge from the coastal section.

Sailing with Spinnakers

A very short but fun and thrilling syllabus which probably packs the most enjoyment of all the RYA courses. Everything you need to know to enjoy modern, three-sail boats.

PLACE SIGNATURE HERE

PRACTICAL

Rigging

▷ Can rig boats including spinnakers and trapeze where fitted.

Launching & Recovery

▷ Understands how to launch boats with open transoms/racks.**†

Sailing Techniques & Manoeuvres

▷ Sail as crew or helm using equipment to advantage.

Perform spinnaker:

▷ Hoist

▷ Gybe

▷ Drop

as crew or helm.

▷ Understands and can sail best course downwind.

Capsize Recovery

▷ Perform capsize recovery with spinnaker.

▷ Knows how to recover from inversion.**

SAILING BACKGROUND

Racing

▷ Has knowledge of courses for type of boat.

Sailing Theory & Background

▷ Understands the concept of apparent wind.

▷ Understands the effect of hull shapes on performance.

▷ Sources of information and apply rig set-up for different conditions.

**Not necessarily applicable to keelboats
†Not necessarily applicable to multihulls

ALL SECTIONS COMPLETED

Instructor's signature   Centre stamp

Experienced Sailor's Direct Assessment

The candidate will complete all of the practical elements demonstrating a competent, purposeful and confident approach to an instructor. He/She will satisfactorily answer questions on the theory section afloat and ashore.

If you sail at a coastal location you can explore the local sailing area, as well as developing your passage-planning and decision-making skills for small-boat cruising. Basic pilotage and dealing with windy conditions are also covered.

PRACTICAL

Rigging

Can prepare and equip a boat for cruising including safety and navigation equipment, clothing and food.

Can stow gear correctly.

Sailing Techniques & Manoeuvres

Can plan and undertake a day sail including a consideration of pilotage/navigation and collision avoidance.

Can use anchor to effect lee shore landing and departure.**†

Adverse Conditions

Is able to self-rescue following total inversion.**

Understands how to improvise in the event of gear failure.

SAILING BACKGROUND

Sailing Theory & Background

Has knowledge of boat handling in strong winds and difficult conditions (practical where possible).

Navigation

Can plan a day cruise in coastal waters, including knowledge of:

Publications, i.e. charts, tide tables.

Navigation instruments.

Use of GPS.

Tidal heights and streams.

Rule of Twelfths.

Decision making including planning alternatives.

Magnetic compass: variation/deviation.

Chart work.

Use of transits and bearings to steer and position fix.

Recording position and dead reckoning.

Meteorology

Knows sources of information on weather patterns.

Understands high and low pressure systems.

Has awareness of:

Changing weather conditions.

Understands simple synoptic charts.

**Not necessarily applicable to keelboats
†Not necessarily applicable to multihulls

ALL SECTIONS COMPLETED

Instructor's signature   Centre stamp

Experienced Sailor's Direct Assessment

Sailors will complete all of the practical elements demonstrating a competent, purposeful and safe approach, and will also be asked to answer questions on the theoretical sections and whenever possible demonstrate skills satisfactorily afloat and ashore.

Performance Sailing

Improve your boat handling and confidence in performance boats. This is an opportunity to be coached, practise your helming and crewing and work on a smooth, fluent sailing performance with or without the spinnaker.

PLACE SIGNATURE HERE

PRACTICAL

Rigging

Can rig any type of boat, including spinnaker and trapeze (if equipped).

Sailing Techniques & Manoeuvres

Can make best possible use of crew and equipment to sail efficiently on all points of sailing in a variety of conditions, including symmetric or asymmetric spinnakers (where possible).

Can spot and use wind shifts and gusts to effect best course up/downwind.

Can perform capsize recovery with spinnaker.**

Knows how to recover from total inversion.

SAILING BACKGROUND

Sailing Theory

Understands how to make use of wind variations and tidal eddies.

Has an understanding of hull shape and rig types including their effect on performance.

Understands planing and effect of rails.

Meteorology

Knows sources of information on weather patterns for the day.

Understands main characteristics of high and low pressure systems and simple interpretation of synoptic charts.

Has awareness of changing weather conditions.

**Not applicable to keelboats

ALL SECTIONS COMPLETED

Instructor's signature   Centre stamp

22

Experienced Sailor's Direct Assessment

Sailors must complete all of the practical elements demonstrating a competent, purposeful and safe approach to sailing performance boats, and must also answer questions on the theoretical sections and whenever possible demonstrate skills satisfactorily afloat and ashore.

Start Racing

This course is designed to give the confidence, skills and knowledge to take part in club racing in good conditions. Confidence is essential if the sailor is to enjoy racing. The course involves the sailor in a range of enjoyable exercises designed to build confidence and to improve skills through practice. It is assumed that every student starting this course has already mastered the practical skills and absorbed the background knowledge at Stage 3 or above.

PLACE SIGNATURE HERE

Physical & Mental Preparation

Has knowledge of:

Food as fuel.

Keeping hydrated.

Boat Preparation

Has knowledge of:

Availability of class tuning guides.

Basic tuning.

Boat Handling

Has a basic understanding of:

Making best use of the five essentials as helm.

Crew (Double-handers only).

Mark rounding.

Laylines.

Hiking.

Boat Speed

Understands how to alter sail controls both round the course and for differing conditions.

Teamwork (for double-handers)

Understands the requirements to develop a good partnership.

Strategy & Meteorology

Can obtain and understand a simple weather forecast.

Has knowledge of clean air, gusts and lulls.

Racing Rules

Has a basic understanding of the Racing Rules of Sailing (Part 2, Section A).

Has an understanding of the basic rights of way rules:

Port/starboard (rule 10).

Windward boat (rule 11).

Clear ahead/clear astern (rule 12).

Tacking (rule 13).

Tactics

Has knowledge of basic boat on boat situations.

Starts

Has knowledge of transits.

Can demonstrate the basics of starting.

OTHER ASPECTS

- An introduction to Local Club Racing.

ALL SECTIONS COMPLETED

Instructor's signature   Centre stamp

TAKE A CHALLENGE

▷ Take part in a club race.

What are the following terms, or what do they stand for?

▷ a. Being in irons

▷ b. The 5 Essentials

▷ c. To 'luff up'

▷ d. Beaufort Scale

▷ e. IRPCS

Intermediate Racing

This course builds on the knowledge and skills learnt from 'Start Racing', developing greater awareness of the key principles of starting, boat handling, boat speed, strategy and tactics, through course time and regular race activity.

Physical & Mental Preparation

Understands the importance of fitness for sailing.

Boat Preparation

Has knowledge of:

How to use a tuning guide.

How to set a boat up for specific conditions.

Understands:

How to prepare a boat for club racing, including:

Hull.

Spars.

Sails.

Foils.

Fittings.

Rigging.

Control lines.

Boat Handling

Has knowledge of how to steer the boat without the rudder.

Understands the principles involved in:

Slow speed handling, including:

Stopping.

Accelerating.

Sailing backwards.

Roll tacking.

Roll gybing.

Boat Speed

Has knowledge of basic aerodynamics:

How a sail works.

How to power up the rig.

How to de-power the rig.

Weather helm.

Lee helm.

Understands how to set up the boat for a range of conditions.

Teamwork (double-handers)

Understands how to divide up the:

Roles around the course.

Jobs in the boat.

Strategy & Meteorology

Understands:

Clean air.

Gusts.

Lulls.

How to interpret a weather forecast in relation to the sailing venue.

Racing Rules

Has a good understanding of Part 1/ Section A and the Definitions of the Racing Rules.

Basic understanding of Sections B/C/D.

Understands how to sail by the Racing Rules.

Tactics

Understands:

Boat on boat tactics.

Lee bow situation.

How to cover and break cover.

Importance of clean air.

Starts

Understands bias, and how to assess it.

Has knowledge of:

How to hold boat on line (hovering).

Accelerating off the line.

ALL SECTIONS COMPLETED

Instructor's signature

Centre stamp

OTHER ASPECTS

• Has knowledge of, and participates regularly in club and open meetings.

TAKE A CHALLENGE

Attend:

⊳ _____ a. Class open training

⊳ _____ b. A regional event

⊳ _____ c. RYA Zone Squad Championships

⊳ _____ Draw three different race courses used in sailing.

Advanced Racing

A predominately practical course, Advanced Racing is all about developing skills in preparation for open meetings and higher-level competition.

Mental & Physical Preparation

▷ Understands how to and the value of goal setting.

Boat Preparation

Understands how to:

▷ Improve foil finish.

▷ Optimise boat to class rules.

▷ Use a tuning guide.

Boat Handling

Understands the principles of:

▷ Steering with sails.   ▷ Balance.

▷ Can demonstrate these principles in taking penalty turns.

▷ Can demonstrate good techniques in a full range of conditions:

▷ Tacking.   ▷ Gybing.

Boat Speed

Understands:

▷ Relevance of sail controls and effects on the sail(s).

▷ How to change gears in different conditions while on the water.

▷ How to vary the tuning guide for different conditions.

▷ How to create your own tuning guide.

▷ How to create your own post-race analysis sheet.

Teamwork (double-handers)

Understands effective:

▷ Race analysis.

▷ Race and training goals.

Can:

▷ Communicate effectively.

▷ React to changing circumstances.

Strategy and Meteorology

▷ Can create a race strategy prior to going afloat based on weather forecasts and tide tables etc.

Racing Rules

▷ Has good knowledge and understanding of the Racing Rules of Sailing, Part 2.

▷ Understands the RYA Racing Charter.

Tactics

Has knowledge of:

▷ Holding a lane upwind.

▷ Boat on fleet tactics.

▷ Attacking.

▷ Controlling situations.

Understands:

▷ Boat on group tactics.

▷ Overtaking and defending tactics.

▷ Covering.

▷ Different approaches to marks – when to gybe or bear away.

Starts

▷ Understands pre-start rules

Can:

▷ Protect a gap to leeward.

▷ Hold the boat on the line (hovering).

▷ Use transits.

Has knowledge of:

▷ Various start sequences.

▷ Recall signals.   ▷ Starting penalties.

ALL SECTIONS COMPLETED

Instructor's signature   Centre stamp

OTHER ASPECTS

Participates regularly in:

- Open meetings.
- National Class Events.

What's next?

Once you have completed Stage 4, the natural progression is to the Advanced modules, or perhaps the Racing levels if you have completed Stage 3. However, here are some other areas of the sport that might be of interest.

GETTING ON THE WATER REGULARLY

Once you have completed some of the stages in this logbook, you might like to look for ways to get on the water regularly. Often the centre you have been going to will be able to talk you through the opportunities with them or locally. But with over 1,400 sailing clubs across the UK, inland and coastal, there is bound to be somewhere close by.

To find your nearest club or training centres, visit the RYA website:
www.rya.org.uk/wheresmynearest

When you learn to sail, the RYA training centre or club will provide boats, but when you are looking to develop your skills you could sail with someone else, or buy your own boat. Sailing with an experienced person is a really good way to learn and many clubs run schemes to introduce new sailors into the club.

If you do decide to buy a boat the best way to select one is to find out what classes are sailed at your local club and which boat is best for your size and ability.

BECOMING AN INSTRUCTOR AND THE INSTRUCTOR PATHWAY

With sailing having grabbed your attention, you may wish to pass the skills you have learnt from this exhilarating sport on to others. Once you have gained one of the Advanced modules, you can start your progression on the instructional ladder as an Assistant Instructor. On turning 16, you may choose to progress this and become a fully qualified RYA Dinghy Instructor.

If you have basic racing experience, you may enjoy the opportunity to learn basic race coaching techniques. The Racing Instructor course covers instructional techniques ashore and afloat, allowing you to assist others to start their pathway to racing!

> Further details of the RYA National Sailing Scheme are available in RYA publication G4, the *RYA National Sailing Scheme Syllabus & Logbook.*

THE DUKE OF EDINBURGH'S AWARD

Are you aged between 14 to 24 and fancy challenging yourself?

The RYA is recognised as a National Operating Authority for The Duke of Edinburgh's Award (DofE). The DofE is a voluntary, non-competitive programme of activities for anyone aged 14 to 24, providing a fantastic opportunity to experience new activities or develop existing skills.

There are three progressive levels of programmes that, when successfully completed, lead to a Bronze, Silver or Gold Award.

Sailing as part of your DofE

Achieving a DofE Award can be made an adventure from beginning to end. Within an RYA club or training centre there are already many activities you could take part in that can count towards your DofE. These could range from:

- Volunteering: Helping out at your local training centre, club or Team15 night on a regular basis. This could be as an assistant, in the kitchen or maybe even on the committee!

- Physical: Regularly taking part in sailing or windsurfing activity? Why not set yourself a goal to gain a certain certificate in the RYA National Sailing or Windsurfing scheme, or maybe participate in regular club racing?

- Skill: All about developing your skills, whether practical, social or personal. You may choose to sharpen up your powerboating, learn a new skill such as boat repair work, become an instructor or perhaps increase your theory knowledge and learn all about meteorology!

- Residential and Expedition: You may never have been away from home before, let alone used your board or boat to go on an exciting adventure with friends, so now is the time!

> Further information can be found, explaining the opportunities available, on the DofE website www.dofe.org, and the RYA website www.rya.org.uk/go/dofe.

Get into Racing

Racing is an exciting and sociable way to develop your sailing. Starting out can be a little daunting, so hopefully the coaching information highlights the key areas you need to consider in learning to race, and gives guidance to help make your racing fun and rewarding.

There are a number of ways to go racing:

SAILING CLUBS

Most racing in the UK is run by clubs, during the evening or weekends. Some larger clubs may have a youth section and many run introductory race training sessions.

As a club member you may be able to hire a boat, or sail with another member, but in many clubs you need to have use of your own boat. Lots of clubs run regular courses and training to help sailors to improve at all levels. They may also host 'open meetings' for a particular class of boat (see below).

Clubs that run youth coaching are often granted RYA Champion Club status. This means that they have a good-quality, safe and effective race-training programme that enthuses and develops young sailors. These clubs have strong links to the RYA Junior and Youth squads.

Choosing the right club will be an individual decision but here are some questions to consider:

- Do they run training for novice sailors?
- Is the sailing area safe for novices?
- What classes of dinghy do they race and when?
- How much is membership and what does it include?
- Do I need to buy a boat?

CLASS ASSOCIATIONS

Members of these organisations sail the same class of boat. There will be an active programme of open meetings around the country and national championships to decide the best sailor of that class. Most class members have a home sailing club, but may also travel to attend open meetings.

RYA SQUADS

The RYA runs zone and national squads across the country to help develop young racers across the junior and youth age groups. Sailors train and race in the following supported and pathway classes:

Zone Squads – (normally under 13/14)

Optimist, Topper, RS Feva XL, Windsurfer

Junior Squads – (normally under 16)

Optimist, Topper, Laser 4.7, RS Feva, Bic Techno 293OD

Youth Squads – (normally under 19)

Laser Standard, Laser Radial, 420, 29er, Neil Pryde RS:X, Nacra 15

Each squad has specific training programmes and selection criteria. Further details may be found in the 'Racing' section of the RYA website or via the RYA Racing Department.

These squads are underpinned by the RYA Champion Club Programme and together form the national pathway for developing and supporting talented young racers. Further information may also be found in the RYA Youth Racing Programme Handbook, available from the RYA Racing Department or your local High Performance Manager.

E-mail: youthracing@rya.org.uk

Personal Log

Date	Class of boat	Hours' experience		Activity and weather conditions		Centre/club
		Helm	Crew	Type of course or activity	Max wind speed	Instructor/coach

Personal Log

Date	Class of boat	Hours' experience		Activity and weather conditions		Centre/club
		Helm	Crew	Type of course or activity	Max wind speed	Instructor/coach

Personal Log

Date	Class of boat	Hours' experience		Activity and weather conditions		Centre/club
		Helm	Crew	Type of course or activity	Max wind speed	Instructor/coach

Date	Class of boat	Hours' experience		Activity and weather conditions		Centre/club
		Helm	Crew	Type of course or activity	Max wind speed	Instructor/coach

Course Certificates

Congratulations on achieving your first sailing certificate!

Stage 1

Place completed certificate here

RYA
Youth Sailing
SCHEME

Stage 2

Place completed certificate here

RYA

Youth Sailing
SCHEME

Stage 3

Place completed certificate here

Stage 4

Place completed certificate here

Course Certificates

Advanced Modules

Place completed certificate here

Place completed certificate here

Course Certificates

Place completed certificate here

Place completed certificate here

RYA Racing Scheme

Place completed certificate here

Place completed certificate here

RYA
Youth Sailing
SCHEME

Advanced Racing

Place completed certificate here